5

SPACE is Volume 1 of the
revolutionary new VISUAL series.

VISUAL Books explore, through skillfully
integrated drawings and text, subjects of
universal scope and lasting interest.
The first paperbound books to use four-color
art throughout, VISUALS attest to the
successful collaboration of internationally
recognized artists and scholars and to
the interdependence of their roles.

VISUAL Books fulfill the current need of
student and general reader alike for a fresh
and readily assimilable method of
conveying factual knowledge. VISUALS are
the only books characterized by this
unique blending of original creative art and
printed word.

The VISUAL series was conceived, and
is edited in Europe, by Frédéric Ditis, with
Heiri Steiner as artistic consultant.
In the United States, the Dell Publishing
Company assumes collateral editorial
responsibilities. Both themes and contributors
reflect the international nature of the series,
which will be published in French,
German, Spanish, Italian and English.

122

GOTTFRIED HONEGGER, the artist who created this work, is a well-known painter, represented in American museums and important private collections. He received detailed instruction in the subject from **DR. PETER VAN DE KAMP,** Director of Sproul Observatory and Professor of Astronomy at Swarthmore College, who wrote the text.

The following are now available as VISUALS

space...

THE ARCHITECTURE OF THE UNIVERSE

by Gottfried Honegger and Peter van de Kamp

Published by
DELL PUBLISHING CO., INC.
750 Third Avenue
New York 17, N.Y.

© *Copyright, 1962, by*
Editions Alpha S.A., Geneva
Visual Books
All rights reserved.

Four-color lithography by
Leonardi Offset-Reproduktionen, Zurich
Printed by
Western Printing & Lithographing Company
First printing—January, 1962
Printed in U.S.A.

The author wishes to acknowledge his
gratitude to the following for permission to
reproduce photographs and drawings:
Mount Wilson and Palomar Observatories,
California Institute of Technology
(William C. Miller), Lick Observatory,
Yerkes Observatory, Lowell Observatory
(Dr. E. C. Slipher), Project
Stratoscope (Office of Naval Research and
National Science Foundation), McMath
Hulbert Observatory, Warner and
Swasey Observatory, U.S.S.R. Monthly,
Netherlands Foundation for Radio
Astronomy, Washburn Observatory,
Sergei Gaposchkin, American Meteorite
Museum (Sedona, Arizona), General Dynamics,
London National Gallery (The Origin of
the Milky Way, by Tintoretto).

CONTENTS

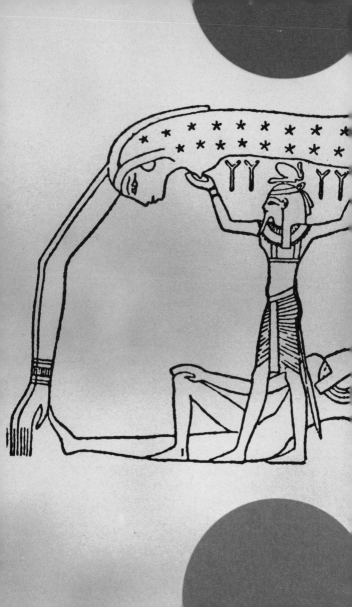

The popular beliefs of ancient Egypt conceived the Heavens as female and the Earth as male. They were united until the offspring of their love, the God of the Air, separated his parents.

As knowledge increased, humanity changed myths to science. Anaxagoras (500-428 B.C.) said: "Put

matter into circular movement and the actions of force and velocity cause it to separate." And further: "First the circular movement started with a small circumference which then increased ... This created the Universe." Thus did the Greek philosopher anticipate the basic physical law which reveals that matter is another manifestation of energy.

Astronomy, the oldest of the sciences, gains its fascination from the fact that it relates man to the universe. Bound to a gravitational prison from which he can escape only through the application of tremendous power, living at the bottom of an ocean of air, man has nevertheless sought to discover the secrets of space and time.

Astronomy first opened the door to the beauty of the universe, whether revealed in the architecture of a butterfly, a symphony, a painting, a star or a galaxy.

2

Fear, superstition and dogma always delay the development of science. In the sixteenth century they wrecked the painstaking cosmological efforts of such a great thinker as Giordano Bruno, who was burned for his beliefs (1).

For Galileo Galilei (2), the highest principle of research was the unconditional liberty of use of the human reason. Thus he paved the way for the revolution of the natural sciences. This victory of reason over fear permitted the astronomer to replace the astrologer and the meta-physician. "Quando potro io finir di stupire?" asked Galileo. "When will I stop wondering and start to know?"

that the Earth rotates daily (actually once in 23 hours and 56 minutes) around its polar axis. The rotation of the Earth furnishes the ideal means for measuring astronomical time. Solar time is measured by the location of the Sun relative to the local meridian.

For convenience the Earth's surface is divided into standard time zones (1).

1

The Earth's rotation is beautifully illustrated by a time exposure of the region of the sky, either north or south, toward which the Earth's axis points (2).

The Sun appears to describe a near-circular orbit around the Earth, at an average distance of 149,600,000 kilometers (93,000,000 miles). The period of one revolution is 365.2564 days (called one sidereal year).

1

Because the planets describe complex orbits relative to the Earth (1), it is simpler to interpret the Sun's motion as being caused by the Earth's revolution around the Sun.

In this HELIOCENTRIC viewpoint (1543), developed by Nicolaus Copernicus (2), the Sun is the center of description, and the planets, including the Earth, move in near-circular orbits, more or less in the same plane, around the Sun (3).

15

1

- Mercury

- Venus

- Earth

- Mars

Jupiter

Saturn

Uranus

Neptune

- Pluto

The planets fall into two groups: the terrestrial planets, Mercury, Venus, Earth, Mars and possibly Pluto; and the giant planets, Jupiter, Saturn, Uranus and Neptune. The terrestrial planets are comparatively small and dense, as if they contained a large proportion of iron or stone. The giant planets are large and have an average density not very different from that of water. The sizes of the planets relative to the Sun are illustrated in figure 1.

The Moon (A) describes a somewhat elongated (elliptical) orbit about the Earth (B), the average distance being 384,400 kilometers (240,000 miles). The period of one revolution is 27.32 days, the time from New Moon to next New Moon is 29.53 days (2).

The giant planets are very cold, due to their great distances from the Sun. They seem to have dense cores of highly compressed gases, manly hydrogen and helium, and finally a deep, atmospheric shell containing such gases as methane (CH_4) and ammonia (NH_3). The terrestrial planets Mercury and Mars (3) have very little atmosphere. The atmosphere of Venus contains carbon dioxide (CO_2).

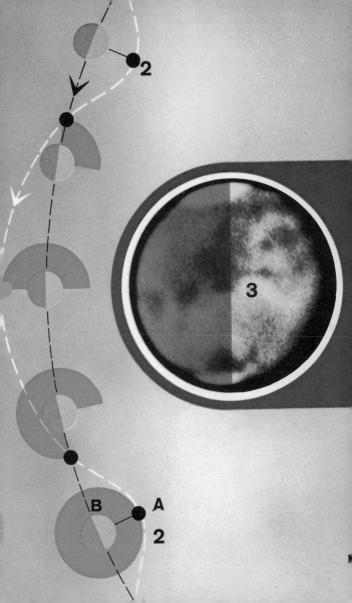

The terrestrial planets have few satellites, while the giant planets have large numbers of them. There is no evidence of an appreciable gaseous atmosphere on any of the satellites, including the Moon.

1

Of particular historical interest are the four bright satellites of Jupiter (1), a beautiful "cosmic clockwork" which is fascinating to behold even in a small telescope. Four interesting configurations of the three inner bright moons of Jupiter appear in figure 2.

these satellites furnish firm support for the Copernican viewpoint: they are a solar system in miniature. In 1675 the astronomer Olaus Roemer noted that this cosmic clock-work appeared to run "late" when the Earth moved away from Jupiter, and "early" when the Earth approached Jupiter. Roemer correctly interpreted this discrepancy as the result of the finite velocity of light. The diameter of the Earth's orbit is 300,000,000 kilometers (186,000,000 miles) and the extreme difference between the Earth's closest and farthest distance from Jupiter accounts for the time difference in Roemer's observations. The time lag over

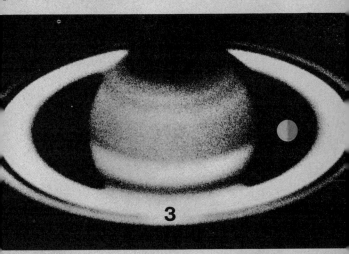

3

this distance is 1,000 seconds, whence it follows that the velocity of light is 300,000 kilometers (186,000 miles) per second.

In addition, Saturn, shown in figure 3 with the Earth in green for size comparison, is surrounded by a few closely adjoining "rings" composed of myriads of moonlets the size of pebbles and smaller describing circular orbits around the planet. Pluto may be a long-lost moon of Neptune's rather than a planet.

1

Meteors are small cosmic pebbles made visible as they burn through friction with the Earth's atmosphere. A meteorite (1) is a comparatively large meteor that has reached the Earth.

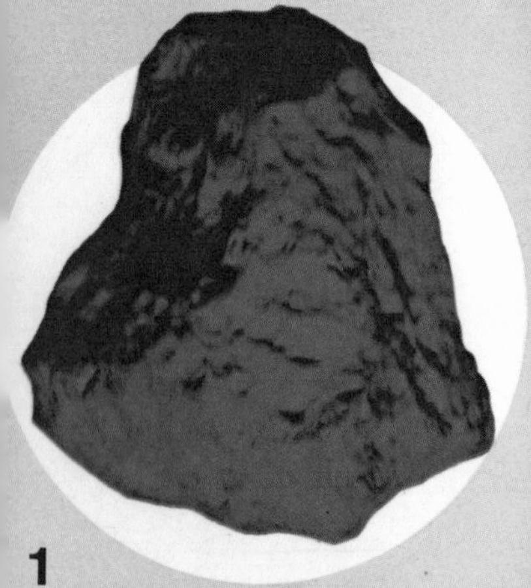

1

Between the orbits of Mars and Jupiter there are tens of thousands of small planets, the minor planets or asteroids. The largest is only about 770 kilometers (470 miles) across; the majority are chunks of matter less than a kilometer in diameter.

2

Then there are the comets,
huge rarefied clouds of dust and
vapor describing elongated
orbits around the Sun, often
tipped across the general plane
of the planetary system.

When approaching the Sun,
the vapor in the head of the
comet may start glowing,
while the Sun's rays may push
vapor and dust away,
thus causing a stream of matter
referred to as the comet's tail (2).

3

In 1609 Johannes Kepler stated
his first two laws of planetary
motion: (A) the planets move
in elliptical orbits (3)
with the Sun (a) at one focus,
and (B) in equal time
intervals the line joining planet
and Sun sweeps over equal
areas (b). These two laws,
the law of ellipses and
the law of equal areas, collectively
referred to as Keplerian
motion, give an accurate
description of the motion
of each planet. For any one planet
the orbital speed decreases
with increasing distance from
the Sun, and increases as
the planet draws closer to the Sun.
At the same time the average
orbital speed of any planet varies
with the size of the planetary
orbit. The larger the orbit, the
smaller the orbital speed.

According to Kepler's third or harmonic law (1619) the squares of the periods (P) of revolution are proportional to the cubes of the mean radius (a) of the orbits, i.e. a^3/P^2 = constant. Circles are closely approximated for the planetary motions around the Sun. For circular orbits, Kepler's third law states that a planet in an orbit four times (2×2) as large moves at only

2

half $\left(\frac{1}{2}\right)$ the speed, thus requiring eight times $(2 \times 2 \times 2)$ as long to complete one revolution (1).

An example: Pluto's orbit is 100 times as large, its orbital speed only 1/10 that of Mercury. Hence its period is 1,000 times that of Mercury. The comparative sizes of the planetary orbits are illustrated in figure 2 (same sequence on page 14).

opernicus and Kepler (3)
ovided the scientific basis
r Isaac Newton's law of
avitation (1685). The Sun is
nsidered the cause of the
rving inward of the paths of
e planets, comets and

meteors. All these objects are
subject to a continuous change
in speed or acceleration,
directed toward the Sun, and
hence they fall toward, or
rather around, the Sun. This
phenomenon is GRAVITATION.

3

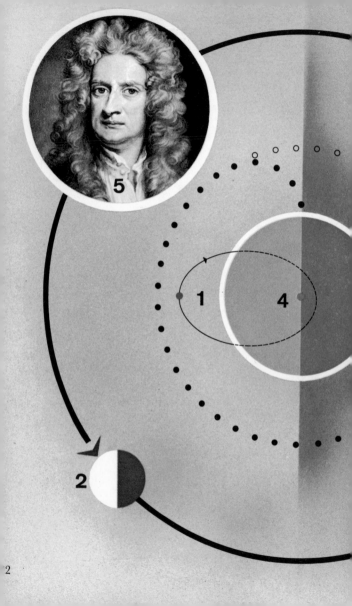

When an object is thrown, it describes a path or orbit, curved toward "below" (1). The Earth is the cause of the inward curving path of the stone (1), of the Moon (2) and of an artificial satellite (3). It causes the falling, a continuous change in speed or acceleration, directed toward its center (4). This phenomenon is GRAVITY, first studied mathematically by Isaac Newton (5). All objects near the surface of the Earth are approximately equally far from its center, and the rate of fall is the same for all objects everywhere on the Earth.

Men have looked at the Moon and asked themselves: what keeps it up there, or with equal accuracy, what keeps it down there? The first question stresses our concern with gravitation, the cause of falling; the second question shifts the emphasis to the law of INERTIA, first stated by Galileo, which would imply a uniform motion in a straight path, leading to an ever greater separation from the Earth, a falling outward. The result of falling and inertia is a continually curving orbit. If the orbit is closed, or periodic, the curve is always an ellipse, with the center of the Earth in one focus.

3

Newton recognized that the surface gravity of the Earth (page 22) was simply the local revelation of the universal law of gravitation, which implies that the rate of falling varies in inverse proportion to the square of the distance between the two objects. This is the famous INVERSE SQUARE LAW. At the surface of the Earth, the rate of falling is 980 centimeters per second squared (cm/sec^2); the velocity of a falling object increases by this amount each second. The rate of falling for the Moon is easily calculated to be 0.272 cm/sec^2 or $\frac{1}{3,600}$ of the Earth's surface gravity. The Moon is sixty times as far away from the center of the Earth as objects near the Earth's surface. Hence we would expect the Earth's gravitational pull on the Moon to be $\frac{1}{60} \times \frac{1}{60} = \frac{1}{3,600}$ that near the Earth's surface, or the same answer.

An artificial satellite at one-quarter the distance of the Moon would receive sixteen times the gravitational pull of the Earth for the Moon. To maintain a circular orbit its speed would have to be twice that of the Moon; it would circle the Earth in one-eighth the Moon's period, 3.4 days. An artificial satellite near the surface of the Earth would have to orbit at a speed of 11 kilometers per second and would complete one circuit in 84 minutes. If the initial inertial motion ("kick-off") is too large in relation to gravitation, the orbit may not be closed; the satellite will fly off into space and may never return. The velocity of escape needed to bring this about is $\sqrt{2} = 1.41$ times the circular velocity needed to keep the object in circular motion.

The orbital characteristics of our artificial satellites were computed by Newton almost three centuries ago. Only recently have these calculations led to material consequences. Whatever the use of these satellites, they move as a tribute to the spirit of men like Galileo, Kepler and Newton.

About 1685 Newton derived his law of universal gravitation from considerations involving falling (1), the law of inertia (2), and Kepler's third law (pages 20-21). A simple illustration follows which assumes circular orbits. A planet twice (three times) as far away from the Sun has $2\sqrt{2}$ $(3\sqrt{3})$ times the Earth's period of revolution, or $\frac{1}{\sqrt{2}}$ $\left(\frac{1}{\sqrt{3}}\right)$ times the orbital velocity. The rate of falling, or the central acceleration directed toward the Sun, decreases with increasing distance from the Sun in such a manner that a planet twice (3) (three times) as far away is subject to only one-fourth (3) (one-ninth) the acceleration.

Thus, the central acceleration of Pluto is only $\frac{1}{10,000}$ times that of Mercury. The rate of falling depends only on the distance from the Sun; it varies with the inverse square $\frac{1}{r^2}$ of the distance.

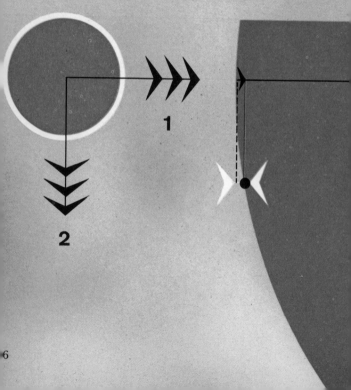

1

2

The Sun is, therefore, a source of attraction for the planets. Conversely, the planets are also a source of attraction, be it ever so much smaller, for the Sun. Newton's universal law of gravitation takes into account the masses as well as the distance between two objects, the force of mutual attraction being proportional to the masses M and m of the objects, and inversely proportional to the square of the distance r. It holds for particles as well as for spherical objects such as Sun, planets, satellites and stars.

First discovered from astronomical phenomena, the law of gravitation has been confirmed by precise laboratory experiments which at the same time have provided the proportionality factor, also called the constant of gravitation, $G = \frac{6.67}{100,000,000}$ also written as 6.67×10^{-8}.

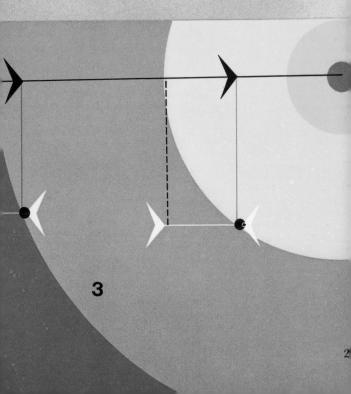

3

The MASS or quantity of matter in an object is a basic property which does not depend on the object's location in the universe. It may be defined as the total number of NUCLEONS in the object. Nucleons are principal building stones of the matter; one gram of water contains 6×10^{23}, i.e., one nucleon has a mass of 1.66×10^{-24} grams. Virtually all mass is concentrated in the nuclei of atoms, which ar minute concentrated packages or swarms containing two types of nucleons, almost identical in mass, but differing in electric charge–the neutral nucleons, NEUTRONS; and the positively charged nucleons, PROTONS. A proton may be considered as a neutron minus an electron, the unit of negative electrical charge, also named beta-particle.

1

he nucleus of an electrically utral hydrogen atom contains e proton around which an ectron is kept in orbit by the ectrical attraction of the oton. The nucleus of a helium om, also referred to as an pha-particle, contains two otons and two neutrons, hile two electrons are in orbit). In more complex atoms (2), e number of neutrons in the ucleus generally equals or somewhat exceeds the number of protons. Atoms of the same or different chemical elements combine into molecules of chemical compounds (3).

3

2

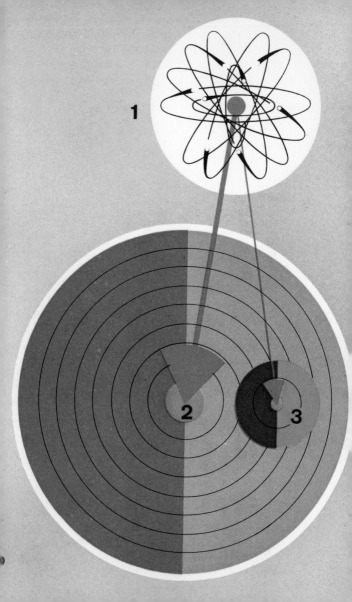

The WEIGHT of an object is the force with which its mass is pulled down or falls.

While mass is basic, and remains the same regardless of location (1), weight is a property depending on local conditions in the universe. The weight of an object on the surface of a celestial body such as a planet or satellite is proportional to the latter's mass and to the inverse square of the radius. For example, the surface gravity of the Earth (2) is six times that of the Moon (3).

The mass M of a cosmic object generally can be determined only with the aid of the law of gravitation, by measuring the gravitational effect, i.e., rate of falling of a (small) object at a distance from the center of the object of mass.

The mass of the Sun is 330,000 times as great as that of the Earth, and 1,047 times more than the most massive planet, Jupiter. In turn the planets have satellites whose masses are very small compared with those of the "parent" planets. Our own moon (4), which has $\frac{1}{81}$ times the mass of the Earth (5), is one of the largest of the satellites.

The diameter of the Sun, the nearest star, is 1,391,000 kilometers (864,000 miles). The outer solar atmosphere or corona (1) is greenish white; its light derives from sunlight reflected from dust particles, and also from rarefied vapors, primarily of iron and nickle, at temperatures of several million degrees.

The lower shell of the solar atmosphere, the chromosphere (2), derives its name from the striking red color, due to hydrogen (together with helium the principal constituent of the Sun's atmosphere), revealed at the time of a total solar eclipse, when our Moon covers the photosphere. By means of spectroscopic analysis (pages 42–43), vapors of some seventy other chemical elements have been found in the chromosphere.

The Sun may be compared with a building. The surface or photosphere (3) is the roof and the Sun's deep interior is the foundation. Since the surface temperature is $5,750°$ K (K stands for KELVIN, the absolute temperature counted from the lowest temperature possible, namely $273°$ centigrade below the freezing point of water), the Sun is gaseous throughout, but these vapors have an average density as high as 1.4 times that of water. Nevertheless, the interior of the Sun behaves like an ideal or perfect gas, since the atoms are heavily IONIZED.

Gravitational collapse of the Sun is prevented by the gas pressure exerted by the particles, ionized atoms and electrons alike (4).

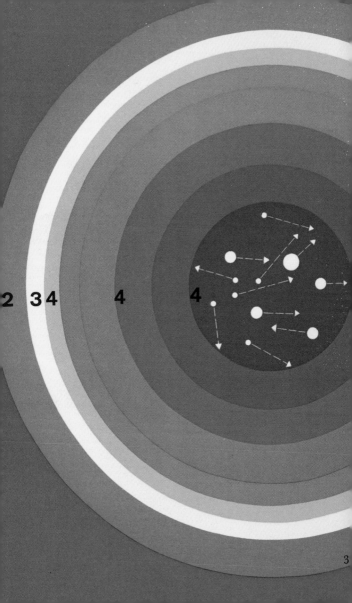

2 3 4   4   4

Outward pressure ("particle power") increases because of the higher concentration and temperature of the particles toward the center. The outward pressure is aided to some extent by the pressure exerted by radiation itself as it works its way to the surface.

2

1

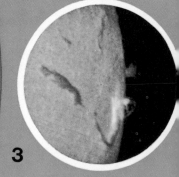

3

The Sun has a central temperature of 15,000,000°K, a central density of about 100 grams per cubic centimeter, and contains some 70% hydrogen and 27% helium (by mass). At the same time the hydrogen is the source of the tremendous solar energy which is continually released by nuclear reactions.

us the high internal temperature of the Sun is required to maintain the Sun's architecture as well as its production of energy, while the flow of radiation toward the surface is controlled by the opaqueness of the solar interior.

The photosphere (1) is a layer of gases which sends out radiation in all colors. These gases are opaque because they are ionized; they are the source of an intricate granulation (1), masses of rising and falling vapors. Sunspots (2) appear as cooler, darker areas, often much larger than the Earth. They have limited lifetimes, usually of several months, and are tornado-like structures of whirling gas masses, outward bound

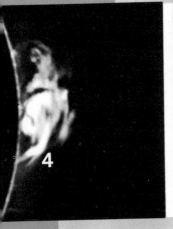 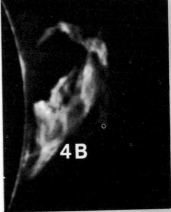

and expanding and therefore cooler (about 4,500° K) with the qualities of magnetic fields because of electrical activity. Occasionally sunspots accompanied by hot explosions play havoc with our magnetic compasses and radio communications. There is a cycle of roughly eleven years during which sunspots increase and decrease in frequency. Prominences (3) are clouds and flamelike formations, composed of hydrogen and other vapors in the chromosphere, another example of which is shown here in two photographs taken 95 minutes apart (4 = 4B).

The Sun's radiation is explained by a gradual conversion of part of its mass into energy.

In 1905, Albert Einstein proclaimed the famous relation $E = mc^2$ where E represents energy measured in ergs, m mass in grams, and c the velocity of light in centimeters per second (1)

This relation states that mass and energy are equivalent and interchangeable.

The architecture of atomic nuclei is such that the combined mass of the nucleus is always less than the sum of the masses of the separate nucleons. This MASS DEFICIENCY is also called binding energy and it is equal to the amount of energy required to unbind the nucleus into its constituent nucleons. Conversely, this binding energy is released when nucleons are brought together and bound in a nuclear package

$$E = mc^2$$

1

here is a notable mass deficiency
r helium, whose
cleus consists of 4 nucleons
protons and 2 neutrons).
he formation of one helium
cleus out of 4 nucleons is
companied with a mass-loss
7%, the largest release
ssible in any single nuclear
ansformation and the primary
urce of solar energy (2).
uclear reactions require high
mperatures in order to strip
e atoms of their electrons
and to cause the bare nuclei to
react with each other.

If it could convert all its
mass into energy, the Sun could
shine at the present rate for
approximately 1.5×10^{13} years.
But since the highest possible
effective conversion of mass
into energy is only 0.7%, the
life expectancy of the Sun is
approximately 100,000,000,000
years.

2

3

The principal constituents of the Earth's atmosphere (1) are nitrogen (N₂) and oxygen (O₂). Aurorae (2), at an altitude of about 100 kilometers and higher, consist of light radiated principally by atoms of nitrogen and oxygen. They are caused by streams of protons, or electrons, and possibly radiation also emitted by the Sun and focused by solar and terrestrial magnetic fields. A general feeble light in the night sky, airglow, is always present due to radiation of upper air atoms.

The Earth's atmosphere acts as an insulating shell preventing violent temperature changes as the Sun rises above or goes below the horizon. It also protects us from meteors, and from ultraviolet and other cosmic radiation (3)—a continuous stream of charged particles, mostly protons, entering the upper atmosphere from all directions. It is opaque to most radiation and transparent only for two portions of the electromagnetic spectrum; the optical "window" (4), which includes radiation registered by the eye, and the radio "window" (5) which covers frequencies from approximately 10 to 10,000 megacycles per second.

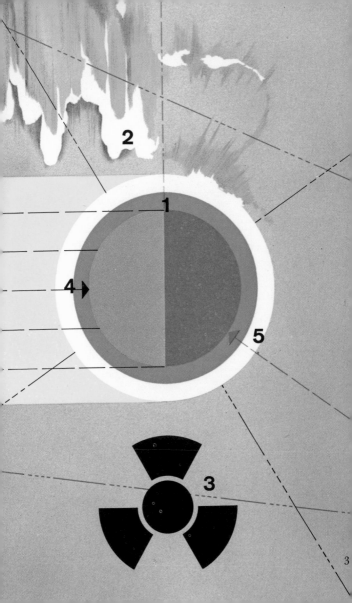

All radiation moves with the velocity of "light" and consists of electromagnetic waves whose vibrations are perpendicular (transverse) to the direction in which the wave moves forward, and have both electrical and magnetic properties. The number of vibrations per second is called the frequency of the wave motion. The character of radiation may be uniquely described either by its wave length or by its frequency.

Radiation has not only wave properties but also particle properties. It may be considered as a flow of separate energy packets or quanta called photons. The energy contained in one photon is directly proportional to its frequency and therefore increases from the radio register to the gamma ray register of the electromagnetic SPECTRUM. The known spectral keyboard starts at the lower frequencies (longer wave lengths) with radio waves, heat and infrared rays; the higher frequencies (shorter wave lengths) include ultraviolet and X-rays, gamma rays and cosmic rays.

1. Radio
2. Infrared
3. Visual
4. Ultraviolet
5. X-rays
6. Gamma rays
7. Cosmic rays

I. Radio "window"

II. Optical "window"

Star spectra at first sight appear to be continuous, and are attributed to the star's photosphere. The hotter the star, the more the region of most intense radiation as well as the star's color shifts toward the violet part of the spectrum. Careful scrutiny reveals patterns of dark lines, attributed to the star's cooler atmosphere which absorbs those colors characteristic for the gases in the atmosphere. Stellar spectra, therefore, are absorption spectra rather than continuous spectra.

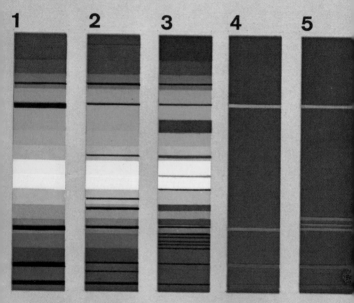

The chemical composition of all stellar atmospheres, including the solar atmosphere, is virtually the same qualitatively and quantitatively. The pattern of absorption lines is dependent on the surface temperature of the star which in turn determines the atmospheric temperature.

Different elements reach their maximum spectral activity at different temperatures; in general spectra increase in complexity the lower the temperatures. The corresponding spectral classification is marked by the principal spectral types or classes, B, A, F, G, K, M, to which 99% of all stars belong.

ype spectra reveal
sorption lines of helium;
type spectra (surface
mperature: 10,000°K) have
ong absorption lines of the
lmer-series of hydrogen (1).
G (figure 2, surface
mperature: 6,000°K), and
type spectra show an increas-
number of absorption lines,
ile M-type spectra (surface
mperature: 3,000°K) reveal
sorption bands, i.e., bunches
lines due to molecular
sorption (3).

e emission "line" spectra of
e rarefied diffuse nebulae
) show a limited number of
fferent colors; primarily,
e characteristic spectrum of
drogen (4) and the green
es due to ionized oxygen.

he striking geometric pattern
colors, due to hydrogen,
either absorption or
mission, appears in virtually
l cosmic spectra. This
lmer-series of hydrogen
es is caused by electron
ansitions between the second
nd higher electron orbits (6).
s universal appearance is
roof of the high abundance of
ydrogen everywhere in the
niverse.

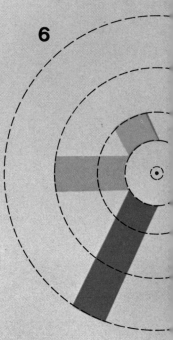

43

The spectroscopic photograph of the star cluster Hyades near the bright star Aldebaran was obtained by placing a prism in the path of the star light entering the telescope, so that each image is drawn out into a spectral array.

The bright stars Rigel, Sirius, Procyon, Capella, Pollux and Betelgeuse, so prominent in the winter sky, represent the six principal spectral types B, A, F, G, K and M. The unaided eye easily discerns the temperature sequence of these spectra, Rigel being bluish-white (20,000°K), Sirius white (10,000°K), Procyon yellowish-white (7,000°K), Capella yellow (6,000°K), Pollux orange (4,000°K) and Betelgeuse red (3,000°K).

Rigel	20,000°K
Sirius	10,000°K
Procyon	7,000°K
Capella	6,000°K
Pollux	4,000°K
Betelgeuse	3,000°K

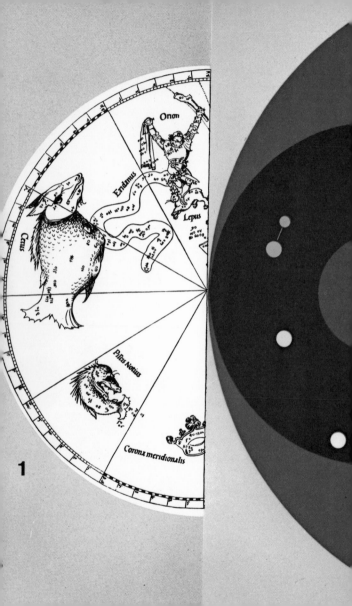

1

Man's sense of order and his imagination have grouped the brightest stars in constellations, illustrated here by a detail from Albrecht Dürer (1). Whether these constellations are "real" groupings of stars or just striking patterns can become clear only as we find out how far away the stars are. It turns out that the constellations, by and large, are accidental arrangements of luminous, comparatively nearby stars.

The aforementioned bright stars with representative spectra (page 45) are found in the constellations Orion, Canis Major, Canis Minor, Auriga and Gemini (2).

Stars differ in luminosity from the brightest (first magnitude) to those barely discernible to the unaided eye (sixth magnitude). First magnitude stars are 100 times as bright as sixth magnitude stars.

2

1

The stars are not fixed. After hundreds of thousands of years, their PROPER MOTIONS cause changes in most constellations. Thus the Big Dipper (1) is illustrated as it is today and as it will appear 100,000 years hence.

Stars are spaced so far apart that their mutual gravitational attraction, at first sight, is negligible. In contrast to planetary and satellite motions, stars appear to move simply in straight paths with constant velocity (2); the larger the proper motion of the star, the nearer it generally appears to be.

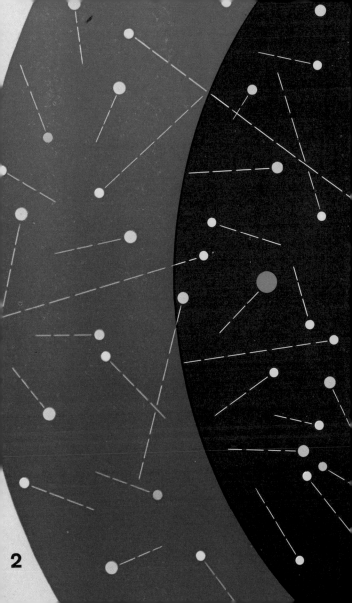

2

To ascertain the distances of celestial objects, we use the surveyor's geometric method. The difference in direction (PARALLAX) of the object is measured as seen from the two ends of a baseline, and the distance is obtained by simple geometry (triangulation). The distance of Moon, Sun and planets has been measured by using the Earth's diameter (1) as a baseline (geocentric parallax).

The Earth's orbital motion (2) around the Sun provides a sufficiently large baseline to detect small parallactic shifts (heliocentric parallax) in thousands of the nearer stars by means of long-focus telescopes.

1

Beyond some fifty lightyears, the heliocentric parallax becomes too small to be measured, and we must rely heavily on the light metering or photometric method. The

apparent brightness of an object depends on its luminosity and its distance; for example, if the distance between us and the source of light is doubled, we receive only one-fourth as much light as before.

he principal purposes of a
escope are:

Radiation gathering power:
e ability to penetrate
rther into space, which is
oportional to the area of
e lens or mirror. Thus we are
le to study stars fainter
an the twentieth magnitude.

b. Resolving power: the ability
to see detail, which increases
with the diameter of the lens or
mirror but decreases with
increasing wave length.

Optical telescopes require
the utmost accuracy in the figuring
of their lenses or mirrors in
order that the radiation of minute
wave lengths may be
properly focused. The surface
should be accurate to about $\frac{1}{10}$
of the wave length.

he Moon keeps essentially the
me side turned toward the
arth because the rotation of
e Moon around its axis has
actly the same period
7.32 days) as does the Moon's
volution around the Earth.

Since the Moon's orbit is
elliptical and the speed in the
orbit varies, and since the
equatorial plane of the Moon
makes an angle of 7° with the
Moon's orbit, we are permitted
a partial view of the "other

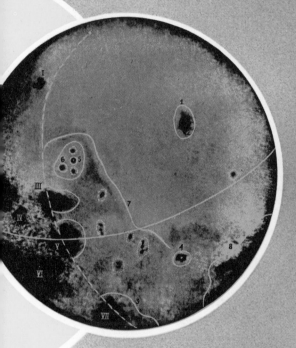

de" of the Moon and altogether
re in a position to observe
9 percent of the Moon's surface.
he Soviet automatic space
amera Lunik III, launched in
)ctober 1959, photographed for

the first time additional portions
of the hitherto invisible side
of the Moon, as it circumnavigated
and passed some 7,900 kilometers
(4,900 miles) from the center
of the Moon.

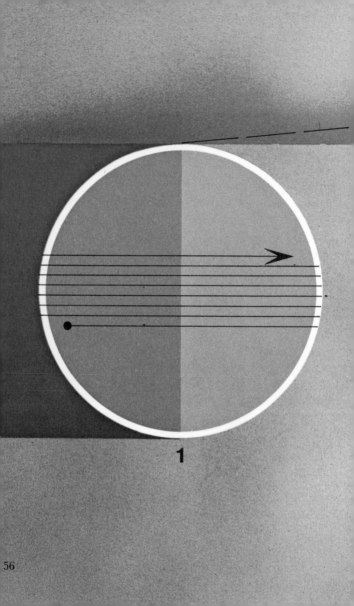

1

The nearest star is 42,000,000,000,000 kilometers (26,000,000,000,000 miles) away. To handle such large numbers, a new unit of distance is used: the LIGHTYEAR is the distance (9,500,000,000,000 kilometers or 6,000,000,000,000 miles) over which light travels in one year. Light-time is the ideal way in which to express cosmic distances and time. Light travels at the speed of 300,000 kilometers (186,000 miles) per second. An object moving at the speed of light would complete more than seven trips around the Earth's equator in one second (1) and would reach the Moon in one and one-third seconds. From the Earth, it would reach the Sun in somewhat over eight minutes (2), during which time interval the Sun would have changed its position markedly with respect to the horizon (3) and Pluto, the outermost planet-like object in the solar system, in less than six hours. It would take this object 4.3 years to reach the nearest star, Alpha Centauri. Thus the nearest star, Alpha Centauri, is 4.3 lightyears away and ago! The bright star, Rigel, is some 650 lightyears away and ago! We see Rigel as it was at the beginning of the fourteenth century!

The LUMINOSITY or
SUN POWER of a star is derived
from its apparent brightness
and its distance. The size of a
star may be calculated from its
sun power and its surface brightness which in turn depends on
the surface temperature or color.

The enormity of space is
exemplified in the five pages
which follow. Next to our Sun,
Alpha Centauri (page 60)
is the nearest stellar object
to us, at a distance of 4.3
lightyears; it proves to be a
triple star. The two brighter
components revolve around

each other once in 80 years. The
third component is a very faint
red star describing a large
orbit of long period around the
binary system. The second
nearest star, Barnard's star
(page 58), is a faint red star
having only $\frac{1}{2,500}$ the Sun's
luminosity. This is the star
with the largest known proper
motion, over 10 seconds of arc
per year; thus it moves a
distance equal to the diameter
of the Moon in about 170 years.

Within sixteen lightyears of the solar system, an arbitrary limit, there are some fifty-five stars which together provide a sample of the stellar universe. They differ greatly in luminosity, color, size and surface temperature. Only four are brighter than the Sun. The other fifty stars are all fainter than the Sun, the faintest star being $\frac{1}{63,000}$ sun power. At nineteen lightyears, we find the faintest star known with only $\frac{1}{600,000}$ sun power. The blue star Sirius (23 sun power) is brighter than all other stars in this sample taken together. The vast majority are faint red dwarf stars.

Over half of the fifty-five nearer stars are grouped in double or triple arrangements. The double stars permit measurement of the masses of the stars and reveal that the less luminous the star, the less massive it is. The faintest star, L726-8B, has only 3.5% of the Sun's mass but is still more than 30 times as massive as Jupiter, the largest planet.

Exceptional stars are the white dwarfs, small feeble objects of comparatively high mass and very high density.

On the average, stars are several lightyears apart, while the sizes of stars are generally well below one lightminute. The diameter of the Sun is less than five lightseconds. The spacing between the double and triple systems is extremely small, well below one lightday. The vast distances between the stars in our neighborhood is illustrated by a scaled analogy of some fifty-five spheres–grapefruits, oranges, tomatoes, raspberries and grains–spread through a spherical vacuum the size of the Earth, i.e., 12,740 kilometers (7,914 miles) in diameter.

If the stars in this sample were pulverized and the debris evenly spread, the average density would prove to be 4×10^{-24} grams per cubic centimeter or about 2 nucleons per cm³, a virtual vacuum.

While stars are self-luminous bodies, planets are not and can shine only by reflected light. No planets for stars other than the Sun have thus far been discovered. Even had the nearest star, Alpha Centauri, a planet as large as Jupiter, it could not be seen with present observational equipment.

Grapefruit	3
Orange	3
Tomato	8
Raspberry	36
Grain	5

Beyond sixteen lightyears we do find much brighter stars such as the red giant Aldebaran in the constellation Taurus, about fifty lightyears away, and ninety times as luminous as the Sun. The distant blue star Rigel in the constellation Orion is an example of a blue super giant star; it is some 23,000 times as luminous as the Sun. The red super giant star Betelgeuse, also in Orion, has a variable luminosity which averages about 13,000 times that of the Sun.

With some exceptions, the luminosity of stars appears to be closely related to their size and color, which in turn is determined by their surface temperature. This remarkable relation, the backbone of stellar pattern, is referred to as the MAIN SEQUENCE. The very hot, blue super giant stars of spectral type O form the upper part of the main sequence, the cool red dwarfs the lower part. The red super giants and red giants, however, are "above" the main sequence. It is believed that they are former main sequence stars now passing through a stage in which their size is much inflated. The white dwarfs are below the main sequence and represent a late stage in stellar life (pages 68-69).

Stars produce their radiant energy mainly by a continued conversion of hydrogen nuclei into helium nuclei, as the Sun does (pages 36-37). A blue super giant star 50,000 times as luminous as the Sun converts its mass into energy at 1,000 times the rate of the Sun, and therefore has a life expectancy of only about 100 million years or even less (in comparison with 100 thousand million years for the Sun, page 37). On the other hand, a red dwarf star $\frac{1}{50,000}$ as luminous as the Sun converts its mass into energy at $\frac{1}{5,000}$ the Sun's rate. It would, therefore, have a life 5,000 times that of the Sun or approximately 500 million million years.

It is thought that the luminosity of a star depends on its mass and age. For young stars the luminosity depends primarily on the mass; the higher the mass, the higher the luminosity. This is exactly what the main sequence stars reveal, and we may conclude that such stars are comparatively young.

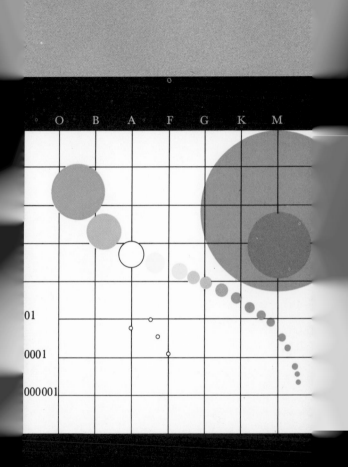

The red super giant stars, Betelgeuse and Antares among others, have a low surface brightness, and must be extremely large. These stars are considerably larger than the diameter of the Earth's orbit (1) but are extremely rarified.

Sirius A and its companion B revolve around each other in an elliptical orbit (2); the average separation is twenty times the distance between the Earth and the Sun, and the period of revolution is 50 years. The combined mass of the two components is 3.2 times the Sun's mass. (The calculation is based on the so-called harmonic relation which is simply a generalization of Kepler's third or harmonic law, page 20).

An imaginary line joining the two stars would appear to be pivoted around their center of mass in such a way that Sirius A must have 2.2 times the Sun's mass, while the mass of Sirius B must equal that of the Sun. While Sirius A is a normal main sequence star, Sirius B is a white dwarf off the main sequence. Except for an outer shell, white dwarfs are no longer gaseous; they are collapsed stars presumably in an advanced stage of evolution.

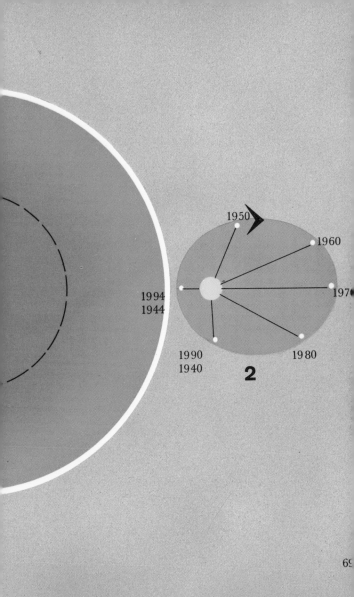

1950

1960

197

1994
1944

1990
1940

1980

2

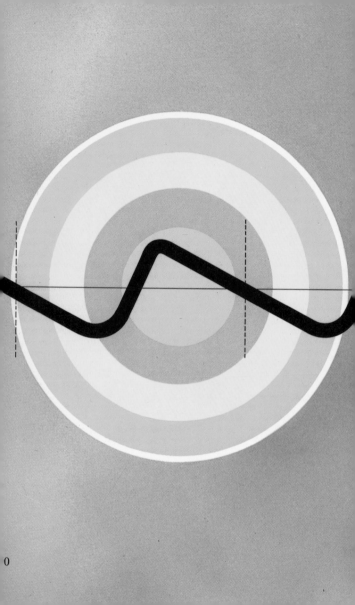

Unstable, or VARIABLE STARS, are important because of the role they play in studying the architecture of the universe. The periodic or regular variables fall into three broad classes:

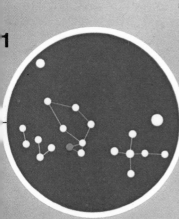

1

a. Those with periods of less than a day, of which RR Lyrae is the prototype. Stars in this class are referred to as RR Lyrae or cluster-type variables since they are found in globular star clusters (page 81).

Their average luminosity is close to one hundred times the Sun's luminosity.

b. Cepheids are variable stars with periods ranging from one to approximately fifty days. Their prototype is the bright star Delta Cephei, easy to locate in the summer and autumn sky (1), whose brightness varies by a factor of two (doubles and declines again) every 5.366 days (2). The longer the period during which the cycle bright-dark-bright occurs, the greater their average luminosity or sun power. This period-luminosity relation of Cepheids admits of a simple explanation. They are pulsating stars, heaving in and out (2), comparable to a pendulum oscillating about its position of equilibrium. As in the case of a pendulum, or any vibrating object, the larger the bulk, the slower the vibration. Similarly with these unstable stars, the larger the pulsating star, the longer its period of pulsation. The large sun power of RR Lyrae and Cepheid variables makes them valuable space probers or distance indicators: their characteristic luminosity thus reveals our distances from them or from the objects such as globular clusters (page 81) or galaxies (pages 88-89) in which they are located. 7

c. The long period or Mira variables have periods ranging from about 100 to 1,000 days. Their prototype is Mira Ceti, a red giant star, varying between about the second to the tenth magnitude approximately every ten months. The variability does not occur with the same clockwork precision as in the case of the cluster-type variables and the Cepheids. No simple explanation exists for the behavior of these stars. Red giant stars, in general, seem to be predisposed toward instability.

The second important group of unstable stars are the explosive stars, which also may be divided into three groups:

a. The flare stars are red dwarf stars which suddenly flare up and may more than double in brightness for up to an hour. These are obviously rather superficial phenomena, caused by a temporary eruption of excess energy through the star's photosphere.

b. Novae or "temporary" stars are those whose radiation increases ten thousandfold within forty-eight hours. For a short while the star may appear as a very conspicuous object in the sky, but after several weeks the brightness has dimmed appreciably; in a matter of years the star is back to normal. Here we deal with a large-scale stellar explosion during which material as well as energy is ejected from the star.

c. Supernovae appear when the explosion is of such a tremendous nature that for several days at least the brightness of the star reaches as much as 100 million sun power. An appreciable fraction of the stellar material is thrown off. While novae appear frequently, supernovae are very rare.

Double stars, whose orbits are seen "on edge", appear as eclipsing variables or eclipsing binaries. Although not intrinsically variable stars, they are of great importance, since they give us information about the sizes and luminosities of stars.

The symmetrical nebulae, named planetary nebulae, may be late evolutionary stages of red giant stars, in which surface layers have been ejected and a central white dwarf remains. Note the jetlike streamers in the photograph of NGC 7923.

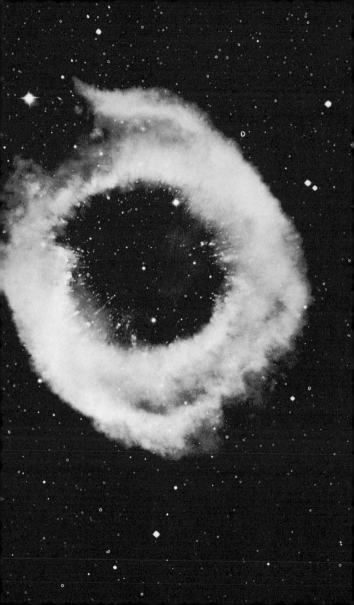

Oriental annals record the appearance on July 4, 1054, of a supernova in the constellation Taurus. At the same location, we now observe the Crab Nebula (1), a symmetrical planetary nebula surrounding a very faint hot star. The nebulous material, consisting mainly of hydrogen, ionized oxygen and nitrogen, is expanding away from the center at a terrific rate. There is no doubt that the Crab Nebula is the current revelation of the stellar explosion or the supernova observed in the eleventh century. Recent studies of American Indian records reveal a simultaneous observation of the new moon and this same nova the day after its appearance (2).

Novae also provide another insight into the universe. A few weeks after the appearance of Nova Persei in 1901, luminous clouds began to appear in the vicinity of this star. What happened was this: the nova light was turned on, as it were; after a while the blazing light of the stellar explosion, rushing at the speed of light, began to illuminate the hitherto dark clouds of dust which fill the stellar system. What we observed was the light "crawling" through space and gradually flooding the dark clouds. It is not often that we can see light move, but in this case the nova and clouds were so far away, some 500 lightyears, that the light appeared to move very slowly. Many years later we began to see the

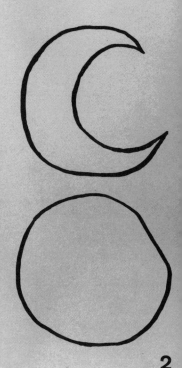

2

material thrown off by the nova itself at the speed of a thousand kilometers (600 miles) per second, a very small fraction of the speed of light.

Our own stellar system is referred to as the Milky Way, the galactic system, or simply our galaxy. That luminous band across a clear night sky, the Milky Way, indicates an unresolved arrangement of stars. The number of faint stars increases in all directions of the sky as the telescopic power grows, but most strikingly so along the Milky Way. At the same time, the Milky Way shows a complex, detailed structure of stars broken by dark patches apparently caused by obscuring material.

Aristotle regarded the Milky Way as an atmospheric phenomenon. More generally the Greeks thought it was simply the milk of Juno, spilled by Hercules, the son of Jupiter and Juno, which had left a lasting mark on the sky, as illustrated by Tintoretto's painting. Others considered the Milky Way as the celestial road leading to the palace and realm of Jupiter. Again others described it as the remnants of the fire started by Phaëton as he wanted to drive the Sun-cart. Some ancients regarded the Milky Way as the trace left from an earlier path of the Sun or even as a belt of solder, connecting the two halves of the sky!

Early in the nineteenth century, William Herschel (1) counted the stars that he could see in his large reflecting telescope and deduced that the visible and the telescopic stars form a disk-like arrangement. The solar system appeared to be near the center of this disk. In the first part of the twentieth century Jacobus Cornelis Kapteyn (2) established that the "disk" of stars had an "equatorial" extent of some twenty thousand lightyears (3). However, we have gradually become aware of interstellar material consisting of very cold dust grains and gases which seriously impair our vision. It is clearly revealed

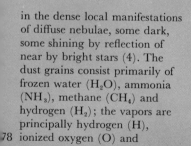

in the dense local manifestations of diffuse nebulae, some dark, some shining by reflection of near by bright stars (4). The dust grains consist primarily of frozen water (H_2O), ammonia (NH_3), methane (CH_4) and hydrogen (H_2); the vapors are principally hydrogen (H), ionized oxygen (O) and ionized nitrogen (N).

The apparent limitation of the star disk in the equatorial galactic direction, and our apparent central location within this disk are an illusion caused by the dim-out and black-out effects of the interstellar material.

There are also large families of stars. Open or galactic clusters (1) are loose local concentrations, numbering up to several hundred stars, with diameters varying between 0 and 100 lightyears. Another type of star family is the association (2), a group of stars spaced far apart but obviously belonging together. Originally closely knit groups, they have dispersed with time. The diffuse clouds usually found near the center of an association suggest that the dispersing stars were born from interstellar material. Open clusters may be the remnants of large associations in which mutual gravitation has resisted dispersion.

GLOBULAR CLUSTERS (3) are huge concentrations of hundreds of thousands of stars within a diameter of about 100 lightyears. Their distance indicators include RR Lyrae type variables (page 71) and the brightest stars, bright red giant stars with a top luminosity of about 1,000 sun power. The total sun power of a globular cluster is approximately 300,000. Hence these objects can be seen at great distances and first showed the true extent of the Milky Way system and our location within it.

3

The architecture of the
Milky Way system is thus first
revealed as a spherical
distribution or halo of
globular clusters. Bright red
giants and cluster-type
variables are spread through
the volume in which the
globular clusters appear as
dense local concentrations.

The isolated or "field" stars,
the globular clusters, and
other objects such as novae and
planetary nebulae, all are
concentrated toward a nucleus
which marks the center of the
Milky Way, the galactic center.
There is no evidence of smoke
or dust in the halo and nucleus,
but there is evidence of
rarefied vapors of hydrogen.

This halo of the hundred known
globular clusters in our Milky
Way system is some 60,000
lightyears in diameter. The
nucleus is some 20,000 lightyears
distant from the Sun in
the direction of the Milky Way
constellation Sagittarius. This
discovery (1919), first made by
Harlow Shapley, led to a
revolution in space-time
concepts of the galactic system
which shifted the center of
description from the Copernican
or heliocentric to the
GALACTOCENTRIC viewpoint.

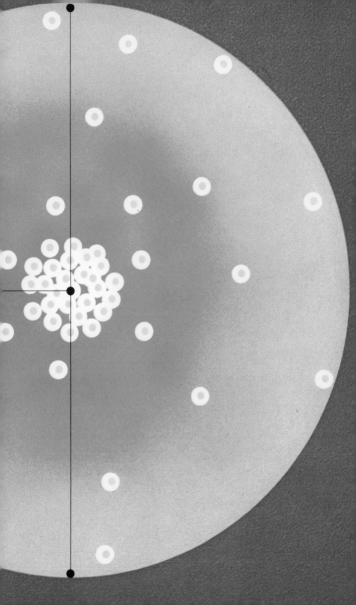

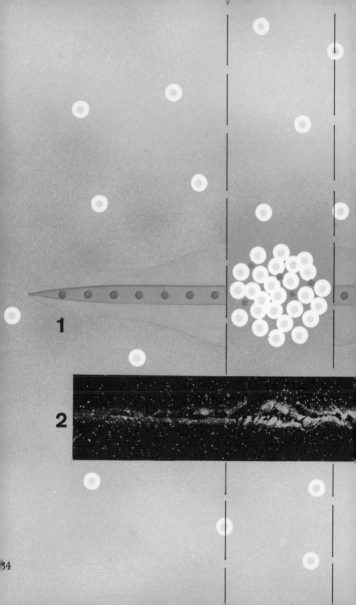

1

2

The galactic center is now also considered to be the center of an extended disk of stars, of which the "Kapteyn system" (pages 78-79) was only a partial revelation. The disk increases in thickness and star concentration toward the galactic center. This galactic bulge coincides with the nucleus of the halo. Conspicuous representatives of the disk population are blue super giant stars of some 50,000 sun power, gas and dust, associations and open clusters, all strongly concentrated toward the central plane of the disk, the galactic plane.

The solar system (1) is located off-center and close to the galactic plane. Notwithstanding the presence of obscuring diffuse material, we observe many more stars along the galactic plane than in other directions; hence the panoramic Milky Way phenomenon illustrated in the 360° drawing by Sergei Gaposchkin, (2) appears wider in the direction of the constellation Sagittarius than in any other direction, while the narrowest and weakest portion of the Milky Way appears in the direction of the constellation Auriga ("anti-center").

Observations do reveal a large-scale rotation of the Milky Way system comparable with that observed in the solar system. The solar system moves in a nearly circular orbit close to the galactic plane with a velocity of 200 kilometers per second in the forward direction, which at present is the constellation Cygnus. Since the Sun is some 20,000 lightyears from the center, close to 200 million years are required for one complete revolution of the Sun. The outer stars in the galaxy move more slowly (Kepler's third law), while the huge central concentration of stars moves approximately as a solid body representing a mass about 100,000,000,000 (10^{11}) times that of the Sun.

Thus the Sun and its neighboring stars travel in a grand sweep with only minor divergences in speed and direction, which are enough, however, to result in a gradual change in the patterns of our present constellations. The dust and gas in the galactic disk participate in the general rotation. The halo stars and the globular clusters describe orbits, many of which are highly inclined with respect to the disk.

Our understanding of the universe is aided tremendously by the fact that the structure of our Milky Way system is analogous to the SPIRAL GALAXIES. The nearer spirals such as the Andromeda galaxy (1, MESSIER 31) have been studied in considerable detail.

The discovery of Cepheid variable stars (pages 70-71) in the Andromeda spiral arms provided the first step (1929) in realizing the essential analogy between the Milky Way system and the Andromeda system two million lightyears away, but nevertheless visible to the naked eye. Similar in size to our galaxy, the Andromeda galaxy is in a state of rotation similar to our own Milky Way system. Both systems have a pronounced nucleus; that of the Andromeda galaxy was not resolved into stars until 1944 (2). The brightest of these are bright red giants of 1,000 sun power, identical with those found in globular clusters, in the nucleus of our own galactic system, and in spheroidal galaxies (pages 104-105). Globular clusters surrounding the Andromeda galaxy were discovered in 1932.

1

The spiral galaxies NGC 891 (1) and NGC 5194 (2) are striking examples of spiral galaxies seen "on edge" and "in full view". These photographs may be ▪0 considered as illustrations of what our own galaxy may look like as seen (1) from a great distance in the galactic plane, and (2) from a great distance perpendicular to the galactic plane.

The large-angle photograph of the Milky Way in the general direction of the constellation Sagittarius shows a striking resemblance to the photograph of the spiral galaxy NGC 891 seen on edge (page 90).

The discovery in 1932 of extra-terrestrial radio-radiation has created the new science of RADIO ASTRONOMY. As contrasted with optical telescopes, the tolerance in the surface of radio reflecting telescopes at best need be only one centimeter. The reflecting surfaces are made of metal, frequently of wire mesh. A large radio telescope, say twenty-five meters (eighty-two feet) in diameter, has a resolving power of barely one degree of arc. However, such a coarse resolving power does not interfere with the important contributions made by radio telescopes because high resolving power is not a primary requirement for the measurement of the structure of the Milky Way system.

Currently the spiral structure of our galaxy is being explored with the aid of radio-radiation from very cool interstellar hydrogen which results from a reversal in the spin of the electron in its lowest orbit. At the same time the electron revolves around the proton, it rotates around an axis perpendicular to its orbit. A change in rotation from the "same" (1) to "opposite" (2) sense is accompanied by the release of a minute photon of radiant energy with a frequency of 1,420 megacycles per second and a wave length of 21 centimeters. This radiation predicted in 1944 and first measured in 1951, passes undisturbed through interstellar dust. Observations with large radio telescopes reveal that the hydrogen in our galaxy is confined to a thin disk close to the galactic plane in a spiral pattern. The Sun (3) is near the inner edge of the "Orion arm" (4), which stretches from the Orion association out in the direction of Cygnus (5). Farther from the galactic center is the "Perseus arm" (6). Closer to the galactic center is the "Sagittarius arm" (7).

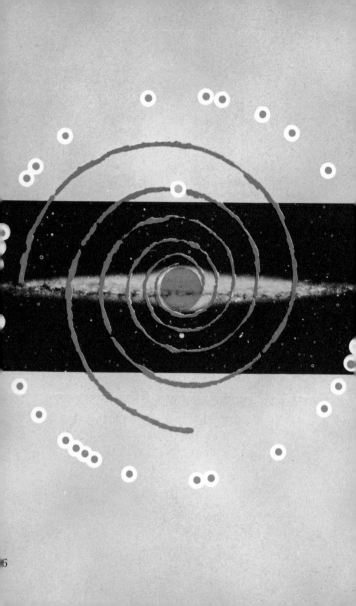

Walter Baade's concept of cosmic POPULATIONS (1944) proposed a simple architectural structure of our galaxy and the spiral galaxies. Bright red giant stars and cluster-type variables are the most conspicuous representatives of population II, comprising the halo, the nucleus and the concentrations of stars which we recognize as globular clusters. Embedded in this halo is a comparatively flat disk of stars, in which population I is spread along the spiral arms. Gas and dust, blue super giants and Cepheids are the most conspicuous representatives of population I.

The spiral arms of our own galaxy are not visible to us since we are in the "disk" and therefore lack perspective; moreover our vision is badly impaired by the obscuring material. However, glowing hydrogen masses and blue super giant stars revealed the near-by portions of two or three spiral arms (1951) before the present effective radio methods were introduced (pages 94-95).

Although at first sight the "disk" is the most conspicuous feature of the structure of a spiral galaxy, it is believed that the majority of stars are in the huge halo and the nucleus. It is only because of the relatively greater spacing of stars in the halo that the latter is difficult to trace, except for the globular cluster concentrations.

The distances to numerous exterior galaxies have now been determined. Distance indicators for spiral galaxies include bright long-period Cepheids and blue super giant stars of some 50,000 sun power.

Some galaxies, such as the large and small Magellanic clouds, accompanying our own galaxy (page 106), are irregular in shape, but the majority are symmetrical and may be classified in two principal groups:

a. The spiral galaxies show a distinct spiral pattern, with two principal spiral arms on opposite sides joined by a nucleus. The pattern of spiral galaxies ranges from open spiral arms and no nucleus (type Sd) through the intermediate types Sc, Sb, to tightly wound spiral arms and large nucleus (type Sa). A parallel class are the barred spirals, with a decidedly elongated nucleus (pages 100–101). All spiral galaxies appear as essentially "disk-like" objects; when they are seen on edge, obscuration caused by the diffuse material in the spiral arms is always in evidence.

Tentatively, we may identify the spiral structure of our galaxy with that of the Andromeda system (pages 88–89) as well as Messier 81 (type Sb, page 106). It is more compact than Messier 101 (type Sc) while its central bulge of stars is less pronounced than that of NGC 4594 (type Sa, page 97); the spiral arms are trailing in its rotation.

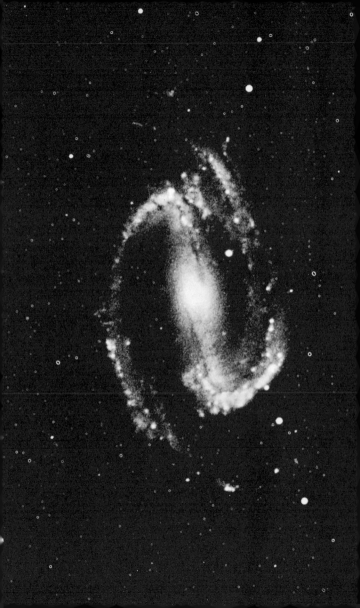

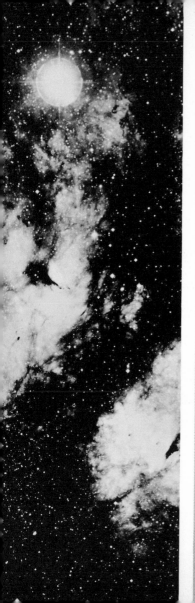

The spiral pattern in the Andromeda galaxy (pages 88 is clearly outlined by glowing hydrogen masses (red Hα radiation) and by dust which blots out the background of numerous distant very faint galaxies. Photographs of spiral galaxies clearly reveal that spiral arms are primarily dark lanes of material along w a limited number of brilliant blue stars are strung, outlining the spiral pattern.

Apparently the gas and dust flattened stellar systems arrange themselves in huge spiral arms in which stars are born. Our own galaxy furnishes nea examples of this process. The most conspicuous bright blue stars must have been born "recently" considering the limited lifetimes of these spendthrifts. Photographs of diffuse nebulae often reveal numerous small black spots, globules (page 103), which m be stars in the process of creation from concentrations dust and gas.

Interstellar magnetic fields probably play a role in the arrangement and maintenance of the hydrogen gas in spiral formation. Spiral arms and blue super giants never appear where there is no dark material, as for example in spheroidal galaxies.

b. The spheroidal galaxies (originally named elliptical galaxies, type E) are devoid of spiral arms and range from a flattened disk-like spheroid to spherical shapes. Distance indicators are the bright red giant stars of 1,000 sun power identical with those in globular clusters.

While the larger spiral galaxies are as large or even larger than our own galaxy, the spheroidal systems seem to be smaller.

The population concept is extended to include the spheroidal galaxies which are essentially nuclei and halo systems, containing no embedded disk. Spheroidal galaxies contain neither obscuring material, nor blue super giant stars, the conspicuous elements of spiral arms.

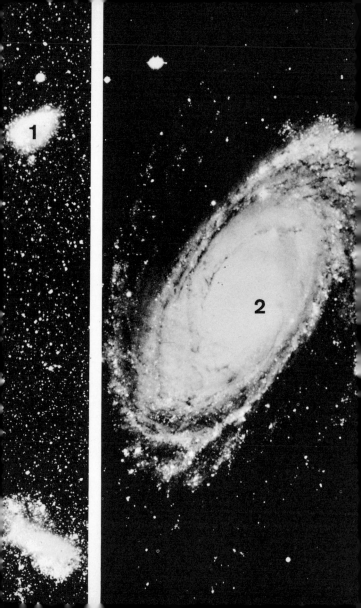

The probable evolution of a galaxy is suggested by the different types we find in the sky. A young, irregular galaxy (1) gradually develops through a spiral structure (2) into a spheroidal system (3). Beginning as an irregular type, spiral arms develop, which are wound up in a nucleus. As time goes by, the spiral arms become more regular and less conspicuous, while the nucleus grows in size. Thus the spiral system through the various stages Sd, Sc, Sb, Sa develops into a spheroidal system, which no longer possesses spiral arms and which evolves from a flattened spheroid (E7) into a spherical system (Eo). The blue super giant stars, relatively young and continually formed in spiral arms, are not found in the older nuclei of spirals, nor in spheroidal galaxies and globular clusters.

As the power of telescopes grows, new galaxies appear in all directions, but they are found most frequently in directions perpendicular to our galactic plane; visibility appears to diminish toward the galactic plane, with the result that few galaxies are seen in the direction of the Milky Way. The explanation is simple: galactic dust causes a virtual black-out at great distances in the galactic plane, and severe dim-out effects near the plane. In spite of these observational difficulties, there is every reason to expect an essentially random distribution of galaxies in all directions up to distances of hundreds of millions of lightyears.

The spiral galaxies are intrinsically more luminous than the spheroidal, but there are more of the latter in any given volume of space. Galaxies are spaced apart by not more than one hundred times their own diameter. In proportion to their sizes galaxies are much closer together than the stars they contain; stars are separated by something like ten million star diameters.

Galaxies appear to be even more gregarious than stars. There are no known galaxies that are alone. They appear in pairs, more often in groups, even in clusters containing up to thousands of galaxies. In these clusters the spheroidal galaxies are always in the majority. The Andromeda spiral galaxy has two near-by spheroidal companions, and two more at a greater distance. Our own spiral galaxy is accompanied by two irregular galaxies, the Magellanic Clouds (page 106) visible from the Earth's southern hemisphere. These eight galaxies plus another spiral galaxy (Messier 33) and several more within some two million lightyears, form a distinct group in space, referred to as the local group of galaxies.

The Coma cluster at a distance of 40 million lightyears is one in which the galaxies, mostly spheroidal, are unusually close together. Since galaxies move, as stars do, the question arises: what are the chances and what happens when galaxies in such a cluster collide?

A calculation shows that all of the Coma cluster galaxies must have collided with one another in the course of time. The stars within the galaxies are sufficiently far apart for the galaxies to pass through each other; the stars may never touch.

Gas, dust and vapors in these galaxies do collide, however. The increased temperature which results causes evaporation of this interstellar material. Thus after having passed through each other these galaxies are devoid of dust and gas. This may explain why the relatively compact clusters of galaxies contain comparatively few spiral systems.

Intense optical radiation due to highly ionized atoms has been observed in colliding galaxies (NGC 4038 and NGC 4039, page 109) while others have been traced because of intense radio-radiation.

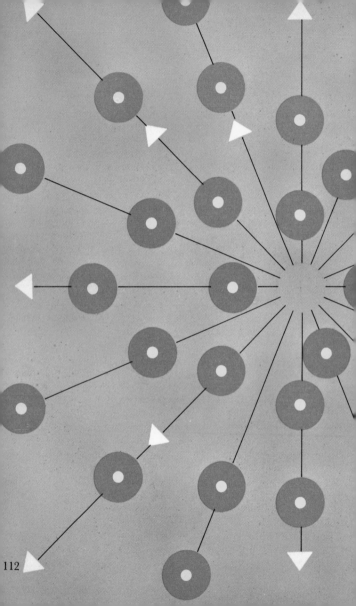

Up to a distance of a thousand million lightyears, some thousand million galaxies are known to exist. Galaxies vary in size, averaging about 20,000 lightyears across. They are some 2,000,000 lightyears apart, on the average, except in clusters where their separation is only about 100,000 lightyears. The masses of galaxies are roughly one thousand million times that of the Sun; their luminosities average some hundred million sun power. Yet if all the galaxies were pulverized and evenly spread through space, the average density would be 10^{-31} grams/cm^3, or roughly one nucleon per cubic meter. This then is the space density of the observable part of the universe. It is less than a millionth of the average density of matter in our immediate stellar neighborhood (pages 64-65).

For some time it has been known that the distances between galaxies are increasing; the universe is expanding. The present spacing of the galaxies could have been caused by an explosion of an original concentration of matter some five thousand million or more years ago.

According to this explosive
theory the universe started as
a huge concentrated swarm of
neutrons. The central
temperature of this swarm was
extremely high. The neutrons
moved at high speeds, exploding
away from each other; after the
first second, the temperature
of the universe was about
15,000 million degrees.

Free neutrons are radioactive;
they are destined to emit
electrons and to become protons.
Within the first hour of
eruption neutrons and protons
combined into the nuclei of the
chemical elements as we now
know them. After an hour not
many free neutrons were left;
protons (hydrogen nuclei) and
alpha-particles (helium nuclei)
formed the principal elements
in the universe.

After one year the temperature
of the universe had dropped
to three million degrees, and
after some 30 million years the
universe had cooled sufficiently
for certain vapors to
condense into fine dust, some of
which still exists in space now
in the form of diffuse nebulae.
After 100 million years, the
universe had cooled to about
300° K; matter had now come
into its own as compared with
14 the original hot sea of radiation.

The gas and dust, by the inexorable laws of nature, split into huge clouds having masses 100,000,000 times the Sun and more; these were the protogalaxies. As the result of turbulent motions and gravitation, these protogalaxies whirled and in turn contained whirls or eddies, each of which had about 1% of the diameter of the protogalaxies. These smaller whirls became the proto stars. They contracted, as a result of which the temperature increased. If they were sufficiently massive, say 3% of the Sun's mass or more, luminous stars resulted.

A different theory of creation and of the evolution of the universe is that of the steady state or "continuous creation". According to this theory, we are not living at a specific age as in the case of the explosive theory. There is no preferred time of creation and matter is being added continually to the universe. There is, of course, no particular virtue in assuming that the whole universe was created at once. It could equally well be in a state of continuous creation. In fact, the mystery of creation remains.

Painting by
Sam Francis: "Space".

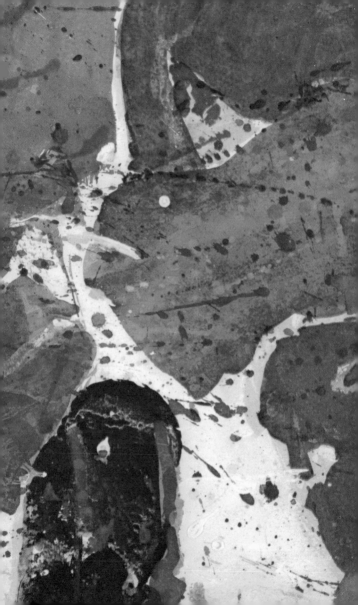

Glossary

GALACTOCENTRIC
Viewpoint developed by
Harlow Shapley in which the
Sun is some 20,000 lightyears off
the center of our Milky Way
system.

GLOBULAR CLUSTER
Spherical concentration of
hundreds of thousands of stars;
important feature of structure
of Milky Way system.

GRAVITATION
Falling of the planets around
the Sun; the universal
attraction between all physical
objects.

GRAVITY
Falling of objects toward or
around the Earth.

HELIOCENTRIC
Viewpoint developed by
Nicolaus Copernicus, in which
the Sun is the center of the
planetary system.

INERTIA
Uniform motion in a straight
line of an object sufficiently far
away from other objects.

INVERSE SQUARE LAW
Quantitative formulation
of Newton's law of gravitation
describing its dependence on
the distance between two objects.

IONIZED
(Atom) having lost one or more
external electrons.

KELVIN
Absolute temperature scale
counted from 273° centigrade
below the freezing point
of water. Named after Lord
Kelvin (William Thomson).

LIGHTYEAR
Distance travelled by radiation
in one year: 9,500,000,000,000
kilometers (6,000,000,000,000
miles).

LUMINOSITY OR
SUN POWER
Intrinsic total radiation of a star
in terms of Sun's total radiation.

MAIN SEQUENCE
Striking relation between color
and luminosity of stars in
our neighborhood, to which
there are exceptions.

MASS
Quantity of matter in an object.

MASS DEFICIENCY
Energy required to unbind
nucleus into its nucleons,
or energy released when nucleons
are bound into a nucleus.

MESSIER
Astronomer who listed nebulae
and star clusters visible
in small telescopes.

NEUTRON
Neutral nucleon, i.e., without electrical charge.

NUCLEON
Principal building stone of matter, having a mass of 1.66×10^{-24} grams.

NGC
New General Catalogue of Nebulae and Clusters of Stars, compiled by J.L. Dreyer.

PARALLAX
Difference in direction of object, as seen from different locations; a measure of distance.

POPULATIONS
Concept developed by Walter Baade, dividing the stars in two classes of different properties and locations in our galaxy and others.

PROPER MOTION
Apparent change in the positions of stars on the sky.

PROTON
Positive nucleon, possessing the unit of electrical change; may be considered a neutron minus an electron.

RADIO ASTRONOMY
New branch of astronomy dealing with radio, rather than with optical radiation.

SPECTRUM
Array of radiation over different wave lengths or frequencies of electromagnetic spectrum.

SPIRAL GALAXY
Stellar system analogous to Milky Way system, with conspicuous arrangement of dust and stars along spiral arms.

VARIABLE STAR
Also named unstable star, varying in brightness, periodically, explosively, and irregularly.

WEIGHT
Force of gravity or gravitation, exerted on the mass of an object.

Suggested Reading

Bok, B.J., "The Astronomer's Universe", Melbourne University Press, Cambridge University Press, London and New York.

Bok, B.J., and Bok, P.F., "The Milky Way", Harvard University Press, Cambridge.

Gamow, G., "The Creation of the Universe", Viking Press, New York.

Hargreaves, F.J., "The Size of the Universe", Pelican Books.

van de Kamp, Peter, "Basic Astronomy", Random House, Inc., New York.

Kiepenheuer, Karl O., "The Sun", University of Michigan Press, Ann Arbor.

Rudaux, L. and de Vaucouleurs, G., "Larousse Encyclopedia of Astronomy", Prometheus Press, New York.

Shapley, Harlow, "The Inner Metagalaxy", Oxford University Press, Yale University Press, London and New Haven.

Shapley, Harlow, "Of Stars and Men, the Human Response to an Expanding Universe", Beacon Press, Boston.

Sky and Telescope, a Monthly Magazine, Sky Publishing Corporation, Cambridge, Massachusetts.

Scientific American, frequent articles on astronomy and related sciences. A monthly magazine published by Scientific American, Inc., New York.